Bob,
Happy
Birthday.
I remember you
laugh so much at
Geech ... so many
years ago ...
Hope you
still do.
As always,
"X" Iris

Merle's SERVICE STATION

*This book is dedicated to my mom and dad with thanks*
*for all the encouragement and notebook paper they sent my way.*

GEECH® is syndicated internationally by Universal Press Syndicate.

Printed in the United States of America
by Gilliland Printing, Inc., Arkansas City, Kansas 67005

Library of Congress Catalog Number 93-060396
ISBN Number 1-880652-19-6

Cover design by Jerry Bittle
Back cover photography by Mike Hutmacher
Edited by Shannon Littlejohn and Eric McCluer

# A note from the artist

The best job I ever had was as a lifeguard. The second best job I ever had was as a cartoonist. There are similarities. Each can sleep till noon, both have relaxed dress codes, and neither one requires any math or heavy lifting. But while lifeguards have tan lines, cartoonists have deadlines. See why I liked being a lifeguard better?

I never really thought about growing up to be a cartoonist. But then I never really thought about growing up; it just happened. It also just happened that I enjoyed cartoons. I enjoyed reading them and I enjoyed watching them, but most of all I enjoyed drawing them. In school while other kids took notes and doodled in the margins, I doodled and took notes in the margins. If I had taken more notes and less doodles, I might have been able to get a real job. Instead, I ended up as a cartoonist. I know it's a silly job for a grown man, but somebody's gotta do it. It might as well be me.

On the following pages you'll find what I would like to call the best of GEECH. I said I'd like to, but there's this thing about truth in advertising, so let's just call it some of GEECH. I hope you enjoy them as much as I enjoyed being a lifeguard.

— Jerry Bittle

# Cast
# of
# Characters

## GEECH DINGUM

Voted by his classmates as the boy first likely to shave. Still refers to the fifth grade as his senior year. He's been Merle's right-hand man for more than 10 years, but Merle is left-handed. The name "Geech" comes from an old family custom of writing names on a slip of paper and then drawing one out of a hat. His brother is named $6\frac{7}{8}$.

# MERLE SISSON

As the owner of Merle's Service Station, he's been working on cars almost as long as he's been waiting on parts. When he holds a carburetor to his ear, he swears he can hear the Indy 500. Others swear he's a quart low.

## NADINE PUCKETT

Also looking for Mr. Right, but at this point would settle for Mr. Left. Thinks temporary water weight builds character, and her thighs have all the character they can use.

## RUBY MOON

Thirtysomething, divorced and looking for the simple things in life — a loaf of bread, a jug of wine and a 6-foot-4 "thou" who answers to the name of Conan.

## ARTIE BEEMER and family

A one-time campus radical who matured into a young Republican, Artie Beemer has it all — a good job, loving family and a receding hairline. Sophisticated beyond his means.

## RABBIT T. FESTER

Not your typical friendly bartender. He's not typical and he's not friendly. Beneath that crusty exterior beats the heart of a real S.O.B. Will Rogers never met Rabbit Fester.

**HOMER PURVIS**

**WELDON LEDBETTER**

**RAYMOND FLOWERS**

**REV. J.C. MEEKS**

# Sorry, we're open ...

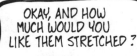

13

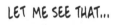

22

24

25

28

40

44

54

55

58

61

71

93

101

121